What the Helvellyn..?

Lakeland cartoons from
The Westmorland Gazette

by

Colin Shelbourn

What the Helvellyn..? by Colin Shelbourn

Published by the Westmorland Gazette
22 Stricklandgate, Kendal, Cumbria

First published 1991
ISBN 0 902272 87 X

Copyright © 1991 Colin Shelbourn

Introduction © 1991 John Lannaghan
Headlines © The Westmorland Gazette

Any resemblance to any person living or dead
is their own fault for looking like one of my drawings.

Cover design by Colin Shelbourn and Pam Grant
Typesetting by Cardtoons Publications Limited, Cumbria
Printed by the Craven Herald, Skipton, Yorkshire

Introduction

Readers of the Westmorland Gazette often ask how Colin Shelbourn manages to make his weekly cartoon so topical. The answer is simple. He doesn't start on it until the Gazette's sub-editors are working on that week's front page!

But it wasn't always like that.

Colin's association with the Gazette goes back to 1984 when he floated the idea of a regular cartoon with the then editor, the late Alan Trewenneck. He was engaged to produce a cartoon once every two or three weeks but inevitably it tended to be, in newspaper terms, a little 'dated'. Its popularity, though, grew and from the beginning of 1986 he was invited into the office each Thursday to inject topicality into that week's cartoon.

It is said that journalists work better with a deadline approaching. And Colin has proved that he, too, enjoys the challenge. He sometimes cuts it fine, however, and he won't thank me for reminding him of the week the front page was complete apart from a small blank space at the top left hand corner. He still made it - but only just! Usually, though, Colin conjures up three or more ideas from which one is chosen by senior members of the editorial staff comfortably in advance of the Thursday evening deadline.

Like all good cartoonists he is an expert at highlighting the absurd or pricking pomposity and this selection of his cartoons from the Gazette, plus a number which didn't make it, contains many of my personal favourites. Even though some of them are now several years old, they have lost none of their sharpness and originality. They are as witty as ever ...and as I reviewed the pages of this book, it set me wondering - if a good picture is worth a thousand words, what price a punchy cartoon and a pithy caption?

John Lannaghan
Editor, The Westmorland Gazette

With thanks to -

Pam Grant and Derek Greatorex for help in selecting the cartoons; Gill Greatorex for expert technical advice on British Rail's logo (it may have a 98% recognition rate amongst the public, but it changes every time I draw it); Bill Goodwin for coming up with the title in the nick of time (and apologies for featuring him in one of the drawings); Richard Belk and Richard North, from whom I have pinched the occasional joke; Dick Rylands for process camera work; and John Lannaghan, the Gazette's editor, for backing the idea of putting this lot into a book. Finally, without the enthusiasm of Alan Trewenneck these cartoons would never have found their way into the paper in the first place.

Just visiting

The advantage of being a cartoonist in the Lake District is that you not only have the locals to poke fun at, but during the summer there are additional crowds of unwitting victims. And they are followed by the entrepreneurs who cater for the visitors by building timeshare estates and upsetting the people who were here in the first place (especially when they redecorate the local pub).

However, even cartoonists can have too much of a good thing (editors certainly can - at one point, I was embargoed from doing any more timeshare jokes). So, just to prove I can do other subjects, this section starts off with the engaging idea that walkers on the fells should take out insurance in case they need rescuing.

In 1989, Brockhole, the National Park Visitor Centre, announced huge plans to build a new exhibition, attracting not a little interest from the locals. Meanwhile, in March 1989, the Cumbria Tourist Board's commercial members were criticised for making money from the area and putting nothing back in (my cartoon so incensed one member that he sent in his own drawing by way of reply; I'm not including it in case anyone thinks it's better than mine).

Also in 1989, a hippy was spotted in Carnforth, fuelling rumours that a convoy of the happy folk was about to converge on Castlerigg stone circle in time for the summer solstice. Police and army were notified and the National Trust erected a barricade of Barbour jackets and green wellingtons.

More exhibitions - later in 1989, Bowness attracted two proposals; a Jorvik style indoor train ride through a simulated Lakeland landscape, and a reptile house. Meanwhile, in September '89, the rector of Grasmere bewailed the loss of yet another village amenity as the petrol station vanished to be replaced by yet another woollens warehouse.

Finally, joy of joys, in March 1990 open top tour buses came to the Lakes, operated by the same company which does so much to antagonise first floor flat dwellers in Bath and York. The Lake District got its own back. It rained.

"Nice to get away from it all, isn't it?"

"Look, we only bumped rucksacks - is there really any need to swop insurance details?"

"You live in Langdale all year round?
Wow, that must cost an absolute
fortune!"

"I can just aboot stand t'new decora-
tions but I'm not right happy aboot
finding these things in me pint."

"No we can't ask the Ministry of Defence to encourage low flying jets to bomb the timeshare development."

"I can smell money ...the tourist season must be upon us."

"Gee, this place is so quaint. You really get a sense of what it must have been like when Wordsworth lived here ..."

"Sorry, looks like your luxury timeshare lodge has been restored to the countryside."

"I'd have thought it would have been cheaper to put a roof over the Lake District and turn the whole place into an exhibition."

"Of course, you wouldn't be trying
to cash in at all, perish the thought."

Q: What's the difference between a
   hippy and a tourist?
A: Hippies haven't any money.

"That'll make a change from all
the sharks."

"I think it's disgraceful the way tourists spoil the look of the area with all their litter."

CS
after
RN

ATTENDANT

LIVING
LAKES

"No, the film hasn't jammed - it's a
simulated bank holiday car journey
through Ambleside."

INTERACTIVE
VIDEO
VIEWFINDER™
INSERT £1 COIN
AND SEE THE
VIEW IN
FULL COLOUR

COMPUTER
CAIRNS
PLC

How to spot a Grasmere resident:
Look out for someone wearing six
brightly coloured woollen jumpers
and an undernourished look.

"Gucci wristwatch, Georges Armani suit, gold cuff links - you've been spending your bank holidays in the Lakes again, haven't you?"

"That's the sixteenth bus today that's gone past blabbering on about the peace and tranquillity of the Lake District."

"I'm sorry, all the stables are taken ...but we do have a rather attractive
luxury timeshare apartment available on a sixty-four year lease."

Getting about (or not ...)

As winter rolls by, the Lake District wakes up to the sound of spring; the birds singing in the trees, new born lambs bleating in the fields, and the merry rattle of road drills on the A591 ...

Regular as clockwork, when Easter is in sight someone decides to dig up another bit of road (and having made a hole and put something in, they then try and put back the same amount of soil they took out - look at the humps and bumps round Bowness, if you don't believe me).

British Gas have been particularly active in this vein in the past few years, with the additional delight of picturesque yellow pipes piled by the roadside.

Go by bus and the hassle starts before you even get aboard. Deregulation of bus routes led to an unseemly battle for passengers between the area's two principal players.

After years of campaigning, Staveley village finally got a bypass. Now cars could rush from the M6 to Windermere without hindrance. Trouble was, no one from Staveley could get out into the fast moving traffic. Calls were made to slow it all down again. Meanwhile, someone at the Department of Inconvenience and Mess came up with the bright idea of doing road works at night.

Not to be outdone, British Rail decided that travel by train was relieving too much strain, so they upped fares to London, just to raise blood pressures a bit. They even laid on an extra coach or two to ease overcrowding. Unfortunately, the idea of a link line with the Channel Tunnel and a big sign for Oxenholme at Dover never got off the ground.

Back at the traffic lights: After weeks of work pedestrianising Market Place in Kendal, laying neat new cobbles and generally finishing off, Norweb decided they wanted to dig it up again and fiddle with something. (See page 93 for an alternative shot at the same story.)

Finally, heroes returning from the Gulf War were posted AWOL after being stuck at roads works on the M6 for several weeks ...

ROADS CAN'T TAKE 'TOURIST STRAIN'

ROAD WORK CHAOS HITS LAKES

Tailbacks cause havoc

'Do roadworks by night' appeal

Bus companies begin fight for passengers

BYPASS TO HAVE VITAL SURGERY

GLOVES OFF IN BUS ROUTE WAR

Road works cause half-term chaos

ROAD REPAIRS STRANGLE A591

Chunnel rail link may be sacrificed

"I'm afraid it's no longer 15p for bikes but we do offer a bar, in-flight breakfast television and duty-free mint cake."

"I said: 'It must be Easter - they're digging up the roads again!' "

"Honest, officer, it's the latest accommodation trend from Japan ..."

"Remember - if you find a car actually moving in the next few weeks ...it must be doing something illegal."

"No it doesn't ..."

"They're so busy fighting for my custom that I haven't the heart to tell them that I'm only sheltering from the rain."

"We've all decided to boycott the school bus - the behaviour of the bus companies is giving us a bad name."

"That's agreed then; in order to slow down the traffic on Staveley bypass, we'll divert all the vehicles through the village."

"I can see a gap in the traffic - quick, get out
and light the blue touch paper!"

"That's typical of bus companies - you hear nothing for ages and then two lots of bad news come at once."

"My bit of road has just gone 'splosh!' - I think we may be resurfacing the lake."

Q: "Why is the 06:43 to London called the milk train?"

A: "Because it's the one BR use to milk the commuters."

"Of course, it used to be a lot worse before BR put on the extra carriages."

"That's a hundredweight of bunting and six months' worth of Lingua-phone lessons down the drain."

Le prochain train arriver à platform deux est vingt minutes late...

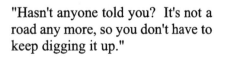

"Hasn't anyone told you? It's not a road any more, so you don't have to keep digging it up."

"It was hell - the heat, the boredom, the convoys of useless machinery, the hostile natives ... give me the Gulf any day to being stuck at Junction 36 for six hours."

Down on the farm (and elsewhere)

Upon being told that I'm a cartoonist (usually by me) people invariably either (a) change the subject or (b) ask: "Are you the one who does all the sheep cartoons?" Answer: "No" (it's Barry Knowles). Just to prove it, this section of cartoons about animals, farming (and sheep) starts off with a story about toads. Every Spring, they have to cross the roads (and road works) to go off and spawn. Hence the green cross code, I suppose.

Despite my best efforts, it didn't take long for sheep to get into this chapter: Reports in 1986 suggested the woolly nuisances were donning capes and leaping tall walls at a single bound to get at daffodils in Dora's Field, Grasmere.

A bird reserve was named after the late, great Eric Morecambe in 1987. In 1988, a survey suggested that farmers were the most miserable bunch of ..er, people, in the known universe. This is patently untrue and all the Cumbrian farmers I know are jolly, happy-go-lucky types who sing all day long and make Mary Poppins look like Basil Fawlty.

The Cumbrian farmer's jolly facáde cracked a bit when the EEC threatened to withdraw grants for Herdwicks in 1989. The same year, odd things started cropping up in milk bottles - BST and snails, for instance. Meanwhile, wallabies were sighted in Lakeland (a rare event, as opposed to sightings of wallies).

Not content with leaping walls, a group of sheep escaped their field (the farmer should have been suspicious when he saw the vaulting horse) and ran off into Bowness to mingle with tourists. It took ages to separate the right ones.

Finally in 1990, a Cumbrian farmer in Threlkeld started selling his drystone walls (presumably to pay for more jolly singing lessons).

A Green Cross Code...for toads!

'Flying' sheep ruin daffodils

Eric 'would have been chuffed' at wild bird haven

HERDWICK SHEEP FACE EC THREAT

'Wallaby ahead' honest!

Farmers are so sad – and that's official

Farmers deny ruining countryside

LAKES FOR SALE STONE BY STONE

Tourists scatter stock

MILK DRUG TRIALS: TOP SECRET

"This is great! I haven't had so much fun in ages."

"This is no good, we've run out of daffodils. Ring up Interflora and see if they do take-aways."

"Meals every four hours, water changed daily, no worries from anglers ...just let the Animal Liberation Front try rescuing me!"

"Naming the Reserve after Eric Morecambe seems to have gone to their heads."

"I think he's taken this report about miserable farmers rather to heart ..."

"Do you still think that BST treated milk has no unwanted side effects?"

"You've got to credit him with quick thinking; within minutes of hearing the EEC proposals, he'd strapped this lot to my head and applied for an Arts Council grant."

"Trouble is, I need my government subsidy to pay for the fencing needed to keep in all the extra sheep I have to breed to qualify for the subsidy ..."

"I knew the Lake District had a problem with grey squirrels but I didn't realise it was this big!"

"Relax, he'll never find us
amongst this lot ..."

"You've had that man from the garden centre round here again, haven't you?"

Local politics (and other contributions to global warming)

If it wasn't for the politicians, politics would be quite boring. Fortunately, they can be relied upon to set standards of behaviour which would shame the average kindergarten. When, in 1986, a local councillor had a baby, I thought her offspring might put the rest of the council to shame ...

Housing in the Lake District is always a thorny problem, largely because people keep buying houses and then insisting on living elsewhere (the south of England, for instance). The National Park Authority tried to stop this with a planning agreement to restrict new housing to locals. The Department of the Environment threw it out in 1986. All this from the party which brought you the free market economy, personal investment and the right of every council house owner to sell it at a vast profit to a second home buyer.

Clint Eastwood's election as mayor of Carmel, California, had possibilities for Cumbria but no one took me up on it. In 1987, the first rumblings of out of town shopping were heard. Particularly sensitive in an area like the Lakes, where the idea is to keep the towns where they are, not take bits from the centres and stick them outside in the part traditionally known as the 'countryside'.

An English Tourist Board survey suggested Bowness would be enhanced by demolishing the Royalty Cinema. Meanwhile, pressure on housing continued to drive up prices. Garden sheds, outside toilets and holes in the ground began to fetch silly figures. In·a public spirited gesture, Ribble Buses decided to ease housing problems in Ambleside by flogging off the bus station at an enormous profit and turning it into flats. The Planning Board demurred and the station remains empty to this day (buses now gather in clumps in the side streets). A newly-built dog kennel fell foul of the Planning Regulations and a modest little ex-council house in Elterwater went on the market for a modest little £200,000.

November 1990 and South Lakeland District Council widened its net of potential poll tax payers by sending a demand to an 11-year-old girl.

The out-of-town shopping debate

Why town stores would be losers

Mark John - the youngest voice on the council

Youngsters try their hand at being teachers

New fears over out-of-town shops

Flat-roofed kennel puts owners in the doghouse

ANOTHER BIG SHOPS PLAN TAKES SHAPE

BIG SHOPS BATTLE WARMS UP

Ex-council house may fetch £200,000

South Lakeland Poll Tax Shock

AVERAGE FAMILY FACES £1,100 BILL

Poll tax fixed at £350 to £360

HOMELESS FACE 'HOPELESS' WAIT

Schoolgirl ordered to pay the Poll Tax

"Order! Order!"

"I hate to shatter fondly held illusions, but what wins votes in Carmel, California ain't necessarily going to work in Cumbria."

"We're practising how to be teachers."

"I want to complain about the number of swimming lessons he's been getting ..."

"That's agreed then. We'll get in a team of independent management consultants to explain to us what our last decision was."

"That'll teach them to turn down my new hotel signs!"

"Well if I can't have my £5 cold weather payment, give me some free AIDS leaflets and I'll burn them to keep warm, instead."

"It's part of our sympathetic landscaping; at night the supermarket sinks out of sight below ground. We got the idea from Thunderbirds."

"Go away, I don't want rescuing. I'm staying here until the General Election is over."

"I've got this brilliant idea! We build all the shops outside the towns and put the countryside on the inside!"

"Hrmph! According to our market research, to capture the bulk of the Lake District's home-owning consumers we'd have to build our supermarket in the south-east of England."

"We've just acquired rather a nice little council house in the Lake District."

"If South Lakeland District Council weren't so mean with their arts funding we could have had a whole hod full."

"I didn't realise it was to save the Bowness cinema ...I thought I was signing a petition for the release of Nelson Mandela."

"When they said they were developing Ambleside bus depot into an exclusive housing complex I expected something rather better than this ..."

"As soon as you migrate, I'm telling the Planning Board about this illegal timeshare I know of ..."

"Of course it isn't a second home - it's a temporary residence!"

"We've sold a lot of these since the poll tax figures were announced."

"Remember - if anyone asks, we say that our calculations were based on revised government estimates and county council spending limits."

"We used to live in a council house until we sold it to buy something more modest."

"Apparently he didn't take too kindly to the Civic Society calling his new satellite tv dish an eyesore."

"We used to keep all the housing applications in a box but things got so bad we had to give it to someone to live in."

"Dad, can I have £6.73 a week pocket money?"

"Oh yes, there have been a few changes round here
since we got rid of the National Park planners."

Going through the motions ...

First off, apologies to Bowness. All the fuss about litter in 1984 led to the first cartoon and a sudden proliferation of litter bins.

In any area like the Lakes, environmental matters are bound to get attention. Especially when the world's nuclear dustbin sits on our doorstep. In 1986, Sellafield started doing its sieve impressions and the beaches of the west coast lit up like Blackpool promenade. We had just got over it when Chernobyl went pop. Walkers were warned off the fells and the price of lamb plummeted when people realised that without the fridge light they could still see how much lamb was in the freezer compartment. A year later, the Ministry of Ag. and Fish was still debating whether lamb was safe to eat.

What goes into the water always attracts interest. First, North West Water dumps sewage into it, then it comes out again as drinking water. To add to the fun, in 1985, a lady reported worms coming out of her tap. Makes a change from fluoride, I suppose.

The environmental pollution which gets noticed first is NOISE. Low flying jets and waterskiers are responsible for this in about equal measure. Since the Gulf War it has become a bit below the belt to criticise our pilots but until they give me a free ride in a Tornado, I shall continue to comment. (*PS* I don't want a free go on water skis, so tough luck the power boat lot.)

Fell erosion is becoming a prominent feature of the landscape. Apparently it can even be seen from space, which should put off any little green fellwalkers.

In 1991, the suggestion came along that perhaps boat owners shouldn't empty their chemical toilets into Lake Windermere (I'm sure that one day the lake will explode).

Finally, yet another firm came along offering helicopter rides over the area. Great outrage from local pressure groups and local cartoonist (who wouldn't mind a free ride in one of these, either).

Big check starts at Sellafield

CHERNOBYL LAMB WAS 'CONSUMED'

Slump in sheep meat prices after lamb ban

CHERNOBYL 'INQUEST' IN KENDAL

Lakeland in Crisis

NWW admits sewage error

Fluoride storm brewing again

NEW DEMAND FOR BAY SEWAGE BAN

RAF PILOTS FLY INTO NEW STORM

Educate tourists
Erosion seen from space

DYNAMITE USED TO SINK BEACH

CHOPPER RIDES DEFY PLANNERS

'BAN WATER SKIING AT WEEKENDS'

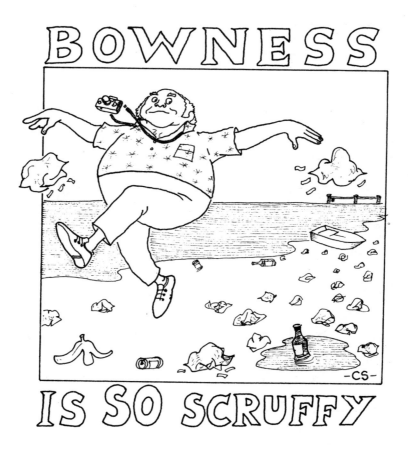

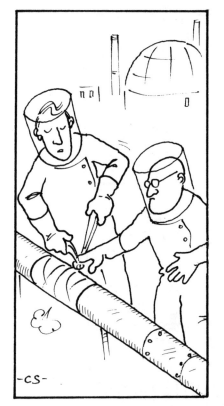

"With all the radiation we've been dumping lately, I'm surprised it could get cold enough to crack the pipes."

"I told you not to keep stocking up with cheap lamb - the freezer's gone meltdown!"

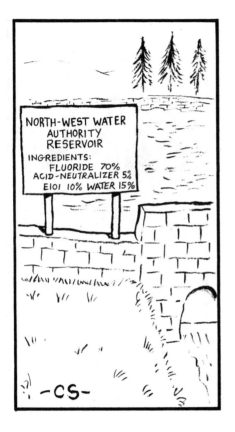

"It's the new National Trust-approved
footwear, to prevent erosion
on the fells."

"I'm against all this fluoridation -
who wants water with stripes in it?"

"What gives you the impression that there's
still something they're not telling us?"

"Right, chaps; this is the revised flight plan to take account of the Air Commodore's public relations exercise in Ambleside."

"That's funny - I don't remember the Langdales having three Pikes ..."

"I sometimes think we'd get less flak if we flew over enemy territory on a real mission ..."

"Apparently there's a huge outcry over North West Water's plans to pump tap water into Morecambe Bay."

"I don't think there's a drought at all - I think they're restricting supplies to increase its value ready for privatisation."

"If people want to come and enjoy the peace and tranquillity by shattering it, I think it's selfish to try and stop them."

"If there was ever a water shortage, no one would notice; most of what's in here isn't water."

"Our satellite photo of Britain hasn't got a hole in it - that's where the Lake District has worn away."

"I think it's to raise money to help pay for the Lake District National Park Protection Bill ..."

"This is our new low flying simulator; you sit in it for half-an-hour, then listen to a tape of pre-recorded complaints over the fake telephone."

"With every boat purchased we're giving away a buoyancy aid and a free tetanus jab."

"I said - it's amazing, you really get a sense of how quiet and peaceful it is down there!"

The other gems ...

I couldn't decide where to put the first cartoon; environment or transport. So it ended up here. You must remember - in 1984, BNFL arranged for a nuclear container to be hit by a speeding train (how many containers of nuclear fuel did BNFL intend to leave lying around on railway tracks?).

Summer 1984 saw the Great Drought. Mardale, the drowned village, popped into the news when hordes of visitors trekked to see its ruined walls as Haweswater receded. Some people helped ruin them a bit more. In 1986, giant slugs were terrorising Cumbrian gardeners. One woman even saw one scoffing her cat's tea. The same year, McDonalds announced plans to open in Kendal; hopes of menus with a local flavour were soon dashed. The glitter of Hollywood hit Lakeland; Ken Russell premiered *Gothic* at Ambleside.

Christmas comes but once a year and at one time, one decoration was all it seemed Kendal would get. Back on the fells, mountain rescue organisations continued to have to pay VAT on their gear, despite being registered charities (when did you last see a Chancellor of the Exchequer on the fells?). Food irradiation (the deliberate kind this time) hit the headlines, shortly followed by plans to update Beatrix Potter books with trendy new illustrations.

As BT continued to disfigure the landscape with its vile new telephone boxes (not that I have any opinion on the matter), two lads from Shap started selling off old ones they had reclaimed. Cumbria suffered a shortage of YTS trainees, dog dirt hit the fan (a regular occurrence) and someone had the clever idea of renting out second homes to relieve the housing crisis. Then a Mystery Lump of Ice descended on South Lakeland. Not from a bunch of little green men slopping G&Ts about in their flying saucer, but from a passing airliner.

In 1989, everyone went BSE mad. Even Siamese cats started getting it (though how anyone could tell beats me). Local schools loudly protested their beef was safe. Kids went out for hamburgers instead. And if you've been paying attention, you'll know what the cobbles cartoon is all about.

BURGER FIRM MAY CREATE 40 NEW JOBS

Search is on for monster slug

World premier for Lakeland cinema

Tourist loot ghost village

New books disgust Beatrix followers

More police for summer

Wordsworth 'industry' in takeover row

Fewer beds at hospital

Rescue team calls for VAT refund

Flu-like bug empties class rooms

Beef still on school menu

YTS 'RUSTLING WARNING TO BOSSES

SCHOOL-LEAVERS MAY GET A RISE

Ice 'bomb'

New cobbles to be dug up

Bin men play Santa

"If our radioactive container survives this,
it should withstand anything."

"Tibbles, Tibbles ..."

"And this is our latest vandal-proof telephone box ... at the first sign of trouble it simply disappears."

"So that's two Benjamin Bunny Burgers, a Wordsworth Wonderbun, one Mint Cake Shake and a DeQuincey Special to take out ..."

"If you ask me, Mardale Show should have been cancelled years ago ..."

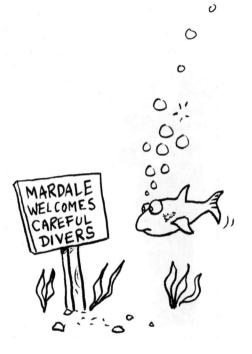

"Drat this high wind - that's the third pole vaulter we've lost today."

"This is good, an exclusive chance to be outraged and offended before the rest of the country."

"You're nicked, sonny, for stealing Kendal's Christmas decoration ..."

"'Ere! I thought some of this looked familiar ...you've gone and done over my holiday home in the Lakes!"

"Do you have to make it so obvious you're a Freemason whilst doing point duty?"

"Ask if the victim is registered for VAT."

"Your irradiated vegetable hot pot just got up and walked out."

"And when Peter got into Mr McGregor's vegetable garden, what do you think he found there? Yes - it had been turned into a luxury timeshare and leisure centre development."

"And this model, circa 1978, comes complete with its original vandal."

"I want to report an offence under the Data Protection Act - he won't let me see what he's written about me on his home computer."

"This government believes in 'preventive medicine' - i.e. policies which prevent anyone getting any medicine."

"I knew combining Grasmere Sports and the Lakeland Rose Show would be a bad move."

"This is the new National Park approved BT telephone kiosk; made entirely of Lakeland slate with a 'Wordsworth daffodil' designer phone."

"Let's come to some arrangement - you support the foxhunting ban and I won't tell the Planning Board about the Velux window in your 16th century farmhouse."

"I don't think you're the festive Christmas tree fairy at all, sir -
I think you're nicking the lights."

Quote of the week, from a report proposing cutbacks at the new Westmorland General hospital: 'Thus a greater number of patients can be treated in the same number of beds.'

"Are you sure this will convince the public that there are more bobbies on the beat?"

"Get back to your office, Jones ... masquerading as a school leaver isn't going to get you a wage rise."

" 'And who's been sleeping in my second home?' said Daddy Bear ..."

"No good. There's never an aeroplane going over when you want one. You'll have to get some ice from the bar."

"Hello - sounds like the 'flu epidemic has reached the North Pole."

"Came in to cash his YTS giro ...by the time he got to the front of the queue he was entitled to his old age pension."

"You'd have to be mad to eat that."

"Wait until he's laid the last cobble, then we pounce ..."

"Either we've been caught in a blizzard or the cartoonist couldn't think of a joke this week."

"Character in a red suit wants to know if we've picked up a brown sack by mistake ..."

About the cartoonist -

Colin Shelbourn moved to Cumbria from Dorset in 1971, but remains an unrepentant offcomer. As well as drawing cartoons for *The Westmorland Gazette* and *Lakes Leader* newspapers, his work has appeared in a number of national magazines. He was chief researcher and co-writer of the first three editions of Hunter Davies's *Good Guide to the Lakes* and is the author of *Great Walks in the Lake District*.

What the Helvellyn ..? is his fourth book (but the first a publisher has allowed him to draw all over).